This copy of
My Own Christ
Fun Book
belongs to:

_____

_____

Written by Susan Vesey   Illustrated by Ruth Owers

A LION BOOK

Tring · Batavia · Sydney

My Own Christmas Fun Book

This book is designed to help young children enjoy the days leading up to Christmas — and to keep them busy!
Fun and learning are skilfully combined. Look for the symbols on each page.

● Some pages can be enjoyed by the child without adult help.

● Some pages need parental explanation, but once the principle of an activity has been grasped, the child should be able to continue with minimal help and supervision.

● Some pages require parent and child to join in the fun together.

● Of course, Christmas is more than just a holiday. It celebrates a real event — the birthday of Jesus Christ, 2,000 years ago. So we have serialized the story, and the activities and ideas relate to this theme as well as to the way we celebrate Christmas today.

It is a book for parent and child to read and enjoy together. Have a great Christmas!

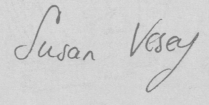

How to make your Advent Calendar

1

Carefully remove the cover from *My Own Christmas Fun Book.*

2

Glue the white area on the inside front cover, between the black lines and the outside edge.

3

Close the covers firmly and leave under a heavy book until the glue is set.

4

Cut along the dotted lines around the scene. Your advent calendar is now ready to enjoy.

5

Open one window each day, starting with number 1 on 1 December and ending on Christmas Eve with number 24.

6

Now colour the picture on the front of the book and put your name on the dotted lines.

How to make your Christmas frieze

1. The angel Gabriel visits Mary.
2. Mary learns she is to have a baby.
3. Joseph shares the secret.
4. Mary and Joseph travel to Bethlehem.
5. There is nowhere for them to stay.
6. At last they find shelter, and the baby is born.
7. On the hillside an angel appears.
8. The shepherds hear the good news.
9. The shepherds hurry to Bethlehem.
10. They find the baby in a manger.
11. Mary and Joseph name the baby Jesus.
12. Later, wise men see a special star.
13. They know the star will lead them to the baby king.
14. There is no baby in Herod's Palace.
15. They follow the star to Bethlehem.
16. They bring gifts for the new-born king.

1

Turn to the middle of the book and pull out the folded sheets.

2

Colour in the pictures.

3

Stick the panel on the wall to make your own Christmas frieze.

How to make your crib

Turn to page 16. There it will tell you how to make your crib scene.

Finish the pictures

Follow the dots with your pencil.
Now colour the pictures.

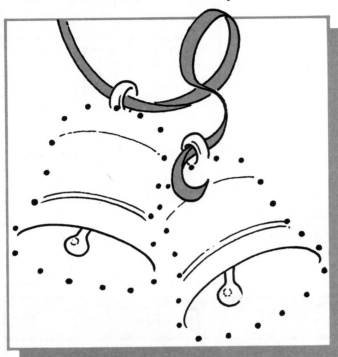

4

Make an angel picture

Tape it onto one of the doors in your house to remind everyone of the angel's message. 'I bring you good news.'

1

Fo... in half and cu... fold.

2

C... ce in half so y... ree pieces a...

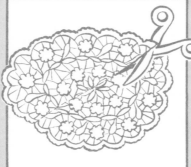

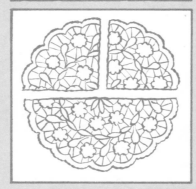

F... ean milk-bottle t...

...eces of doiley ...t of coloured

...ilk-bottle top to ...head.

...me more glue ...le glitter over ...re.

Mary's exciting secret

This is a true story about something that happened a long, long time ago: something so special that people all over the world remember it every year at Christmas.

In a small village called Nazareth lived a young woman named Mary. She was going to be married to Joseph, a carpenter. One day, before they were married, an angel came to Mary with a message from God.

'Don't be afraid, Mary,' he said. 'God has chosen you to be the mother of his son. He will grow up to be a king and you are to call him Jesus.'

The angel left and Mary thought about what he had said. Mary knew that every name had a special meaning. 'Jesus' meant 'the one who saves others'. Mary gasped as she realized that God's Son was to be *her* son. She now knew that God had a special plan for Jesus' life. She thanked God for choosing her to be the mother of Jesus.

The angel came to tell Joseph, too, that Mary was going to be the mother of God's own son.

So Joseph and Mary were married.

Join up the same

Draw a line with your pencil between the two things that look the same. The first one is done for you.

Now colour the pictures.

6

the crumbs

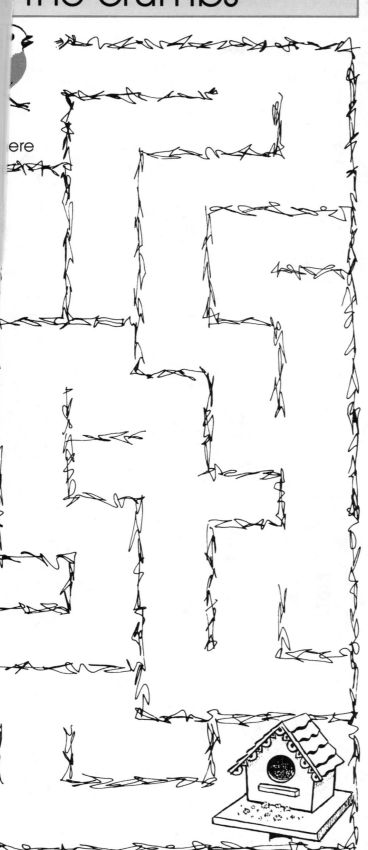

ere

The journey to Bethlehem

The village of Nazareth, where Mary and Joseph lived, was in a country called Judea in the Roman Empire.

One day, not long before Mary was due to have her baby, Joseph told her that the Roman ruler wanted all the people in the country to go back to their home towns to be counted.

All the roads were busy as everyone set off — people on horses, people in carts, people on donkeys, people on foot. Hundreds of people were travelling to their home towns.

Joseph's family came from Bethlehem. It was a long way from Nazareth. It would take several days to get there.

Mary and Joseph got ready for their long journey. Soon they set off for Bethlehem.

Odd one out

Cross out the picture on the shelf that is different from the others. Colour all the other pictures.

Dress the carol singer

Draw a line with your pencil between each item of clothing and the place it should go. The first one is done for you.

A bed in the straw

Mary and Joseph travelled for many days. When they arrived in Bethlehem they were very, very tired and they could not find anywhere to stay. So many people had come to Bethlehem that all the rooms were full.

Joseph knew that Mary needed somewhere to rest. It was nearly time for the baby to be born. At last they found a place to stay. They had to share with some animals, but there was soft straw to lie on.

A few days later, Mary's son was born. She wrapped Jesus up warmly and put him in the manger filled with hay.

9

Christmas shapes

OBLONGS

Let's look at shapes.
Two short and two long.
If you find one of these.
it's called an **oblong**.

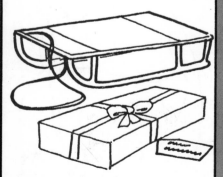

A toaster, a butterdish,
a doormat or book.
Oblongs are everywhere
if only you look.

TRIANGLES

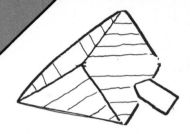

Let's look at shapes.
This one is new.
Join up three sides
for a **triangle** true.

At afternoon tea
you can spot such a shape.
Sandwiches, cheese
or a small piece of cake.

The **triangle** only
has one special fame;
To a musical instrument
it has given its name.

SQUARES

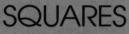

Let's look at shapes.
Look here and there.
The shape we are hunting
is known as the **square**.

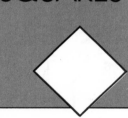

Look for a shape where
the sides are the same.
There must be four sides,
like a window pane.

Look at stamps, tabletops,
cushions and chairs.
Check them all out and
see if they're **squares**.

Use the space to draw other things that are squares, oblongs, triangles and circles.

The light in the sky

On the night Jesus was born, some shepherds were out on the hills near Bethlehem, looking after their sheep. It was cold, and very dark.

Suddenly, the sky was filled with a bright and shining light. An angel from God came to tell them some good news. At first, the shepherds were afraid.

'Don't be frightened,' said the angel. 'I am here to tell you that a very special baby has been born in Bethlehem tonight. If you go and look, you will find him wrapped in warm clothes and lying in a manger.'

Then the sky was full of hundreds of singing angels. 'Glory to God in the highest,' they sang, 'and peace to people on earth!'

Then the angels went away — but the shepherds hurried off to Bethlehem.

They found Mary and Joseph, and the baby lying in a manger, just as the angel had said.

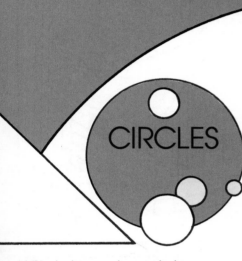

CIRCLES

Let's look at shapes.
What can we see?
What shape is left
by a wet mug of tea?

What shape is a plate,
or a saucer or cake?
What shape on the tree
does a bright bauble make?

What shape is the black
that you see in your eye?
What shape the full moon
in the dark night sky?

What shape is your mouth
when you whistle a tune?
If you try very hard, you'll
guess the shape soon.

This is a **round** shape,
a **circle** or ball.
Keep your eyes open —
see lots of them all.

How many shapes?

Count how many squares, oblongs, triangles and circles there are in the picture.
Put the number in the boxes.

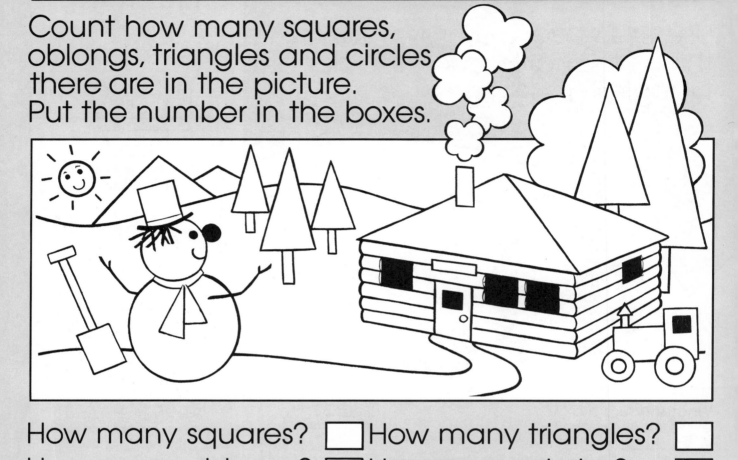

How many squares? ☐ How many triangles? ☐
How many oblongs? ☐ How many circles? ☐

Who got what?

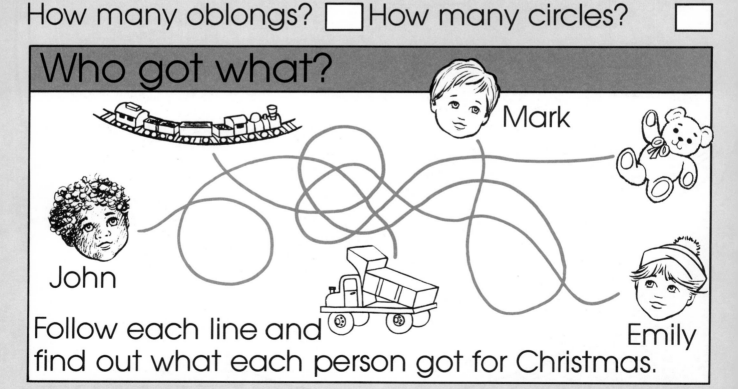

Mark

John

Emily

Follow each line and find out what each person got for Christmas.

13

Christmas counting game

Count how many things there are.

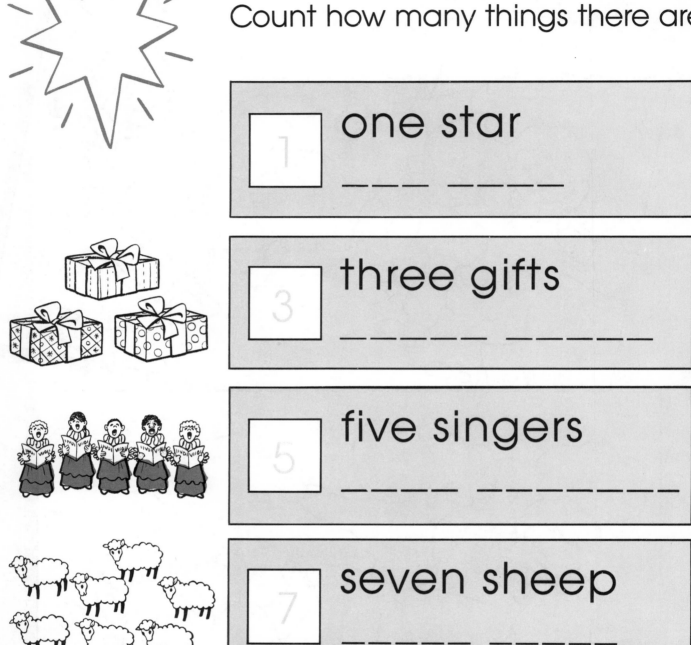

1	one star
	___ ____

3	three gifts
	_____ _____

5	five singers
	____ _____

7	seven sheep
	_____ _____

9	nine robins
	____ _____

Copy the numbers and letters in the boxes.

2 two candles
___ _____

4 four bells
____ _____

6 six trees
___ _____

8 eight snowmen
_____ _____

10 ten snowflakes
___ _____

Christmas crib

To make your own crib scene, pop out some of the characters from the centre pages. Follow this guide to make sure you choose the ones you need.

Glue a small box onto the back of each pop-out character.

or
Bend a strip of card into an 'L' shape.

Glue one side of the 'L' to the back.

The pop-out characters can now stand up.

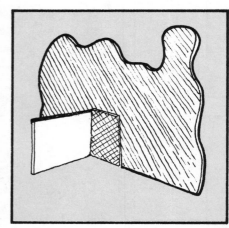

Cards to make

Make these special cards to send to your friends and family.

Pop-out card

1
Pop out the rest of the characters from the card in the middle of the book.

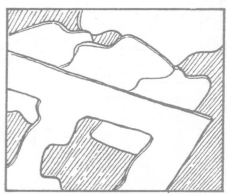

2
Cut out a piece of card bigger than the pop-out shape.

3
Glue it on to the card. Leave it to dry.

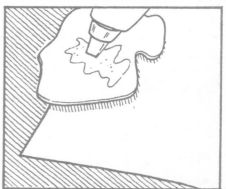

16

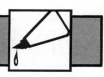

Cows

Donkeys

The baby Jesus

Mary and Joseph

Arrange the pop-outs into a scene on top of a table or window ledge.

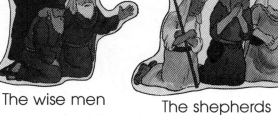

The wise men

The shepherds

Innkeeper

Snowman card

1

Glue a snowman shape on a piece of coloured card.

2

Stick on some cotton wool.

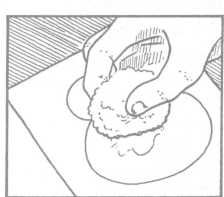

3

Use a felt-tip pen to draw on eyes, mouth, hat and buttons.

4

Glue the background. Put on some glitter to make the snow.

On the first day of Christmas

Ask someone to teach you the tune to this Christmas song. It belongs to the time when people celebrated Christmas for 12 days.

Copy the numbers into the boxes.

Then colour the pictures.

1 ☐ 1st ☐

On the first day of Christmas
my true love sent to me
a partridge in a pear tree.

2 ☐ 2nd ☐

On the second day of Christmas
my true love sent to me
two turtle doves
and a partridge in a pear tree.

3 ☐ 3rd ☐

On the third day of Christmas
my true love sent to me
three French hens, two turtle doves
and a partridge in a pear tree.

4 ☐ 4th ☐

On the fourth day of Christmas
my true love sent to me
four colly birds,
three French hens, two turtle doves
and a partridge in a pear tree.

5 ☐ 5th ☐

On the fifth day of Christmas
my true love sent to me
five gold rings, four colly birds,
three French hens, two turtle doves
and a partridge in a pear tree.

6 ☐ 6th ☐

On the sixth day of Christmas
my true love sent to me
six geese a-laying,
five gold rings, four colly birds,
three French hens, two turtle doves
and a partridge in a pear tree.

7 ☐ 7th ☐

On the seventh day of Christmas
my true love sent to me
seven swans a-swimming,
six geese a-laying,
five gold rings, four colly birds,
three French hens, two turtle doves
and a partridge in a pear tree.

8 ☐ 8th ☐

On the eighth day of Christmas
my true love sent to me
eight maids a-milking,
seven swans a-swimming,
six geese a-laying,
five gold rings,   four colly birds,
three French hens, two turtle doves
and a partridge in a pear tree.

10 ☐ 10th ☐

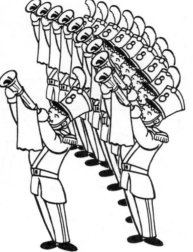

On the tenth day of Christmas
my true love sent to me
ten pipers piping,
nine drummers drumming,
eight maids a-milking,
seven swans a-swimming,
six geese a-laying,
five gold rings, four colly birds,
three French hens, two turtle doves
and a partridge in a pear tree.

12 ☐ 12th ☐

On the twelfth day of Christmas
my true love sent to me
twelve lords a-leaping,
eleven ladies dancing,
ten pipers piping,
nine drummers drumming,
eight maids a-milking,
seven swans a-swimming,
six geese a-laying,
five gold rings, four colly birds,
three French hens, two turtle doves
and a partridge in a pear tree.

9 ☐ 9th ☐

On the ninth day of Christmas
my true love sent to me
nine drummers drumming,
eight maids a-milking,
seven swans a-swimming,
six geese a-laying,
five gold rings, four colly birds,
three French hens,
two turtle doves
and a partridge
in a pear tree.

11 ☐ 11th ☐

On the eleventh day of Christmas
my true love sent to me
eleven ladies dancing,
ten pipers piping,
nine drummers drumming,
eight maids a-milking,
seven swans a-swimming,
six geese a-laying,
five gold rings, four colly birds,
three French hens, two turtle doves
and a partridge in a pear tree.

Picture present

Make this picture to give as a present.

How to make the picture

1 Ask for an old lid from a cheese spread box or margarine tub.

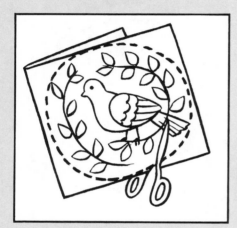

2 Cut out a picture from an old Christmas card or magazine.

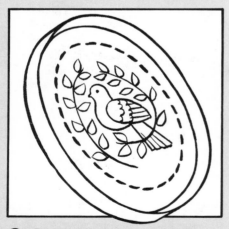

3 Put the picture in the middle of the lid. Draw a large circle round the picture with a pencil.

4 Cut just inside the pencil line.

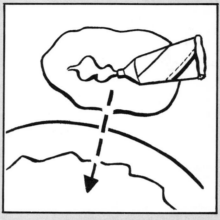

5 Glue the picture in place.

6 Tear small pieces of tissue paper and screw them up loosely.

7 Glue them round the inside edge of the lid. Use different colours if you can.

8 Dab on some glue and sprinkle glitter over the picture.

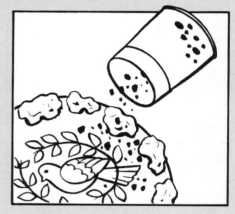

9 Tape a loop of ribbon on the back so the picture can be hung up.

20

Odd one out

Look at each picture.
Each one should be the same.
Draw a circle around the one that is different.

Paperchains

Make these pretty paperchains to decorate your house this Christmas. They are easy to make and fun to do.

1
Find some coloured paper, or old colour magazines.

2
Cut out thin strips about as long as the width of this page. Make them all the same size.

3
Make a circle out of one strip. Overlap the edges and stick or staple them together.

Join them up!

fat candle

big star

short scarf

thin candle

small present

Draw a line with your pencil between the opposites.

4

Link the second strip through the first circle. Overlap the edges and stick or staple them together.

5

Go on in this way until your paperchain is as long as you want it.

little star

long scarf

large present

A visit to the temple

When Jesus was about six weeks old, Mary and Joseph took him to the temple in Jerusalem to thank God for their special baby.

In the temple was an old man called Simeon. God had promised him that one day he would see the king that God would send.

As Simeon took Jesus in his arms to say the prayer of thanks, he knew that this baby was different; this was the king he had been waiting for.

'Now I shall die a happy man,' said Simeon, 'because God has kept his promise and allowed me to see Jesus, the one who will save his people.'

23

Christmas puzzle

star

☐

☐ spears

How many of the
following things can
you find in the picture?

mice

☐

windows

☐

wise men

☐

☐ tree

☐ hats

☐ chest

☐ camel

24

Crown for a king

Make a crown to wear at your Christmas party.

1 Measure round your head with a piece of paper.

2 Cut out an oblong of card or stiff paper a bit longer than this.

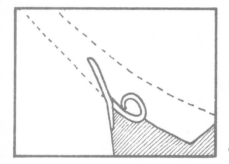

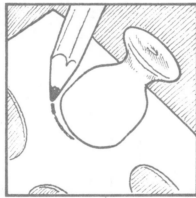

3 Find some stiff card in a bright colour.

4 Cut out some triangles.

5 Draw round an egg cup and cut out some large circles.

6 Draw round a coin and cut out some small circles.

7 Glue or staple the small circles on to the other shapes.

8 Glue or staple the triangles, large circles and squares onto the oblong.

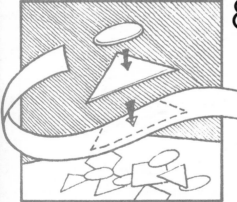

9 Staple the ends of the oblong together and wear your crown.

Following the star

Not long after Jesus was born, some important men arrived in Jerusalem and asked where they could find the baby king.

The wise men came from a land far away. They had seen a bright new star in the sky. This could mean only one thing — a king had been born.

They set out on the journey, travelling until the star seemed to be shining right above them. The big city of Jerusalem was nearby, so they went there to look for the baby king.

A wicked king, called Herod, lived in the palace in Jerusalem. When he heard why the wise men had come, he was not happy. Herod liked being the king, and the thought of another king in his country — even a baby king — made him very angry indeed.

King Herod wanted to find out exactly where this special king might be born. Soon the answer was found. Bethlehem was the place.

King Herod asked the wise men all about the star and their journey. He pretended to be interested. He told them to go and look for the baby in Bethlehem. 'Remember to come back and tell me when you have found him,' said Herod.

But the wicked King Herod meant to make sure that Jesus did not become king.

Christmas finger painting

Finish the pictures below.

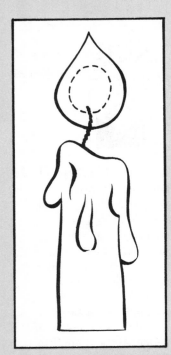

Dip your finger in red paint. Put your fingerprint over the dotted lines to finish the pictures.

Gift wrap

How many gifts are there?

Can you guess what they are?

Now colour the picture.

Gifts for a king

Later that evening, the wise men left the palace and walked through the streets of Jerusalem until they found the road to Bethlehem.

The star they had followed for such a long time seemed to go in front of them. At last, the star stopped over a house. The wise men went in and found the baby they had come all this way to see.

They knelt down in front of Jesus and gave him the presents they had brought — gold and frankincense and myrrh. These were special gifts for a very special baby king.

The wise men left Bethlehem, but they did not go back to the palace.

God warned them not to tell King Herod where the baby was, and so they went back to their own country by another road.

God also told Joseph to take Mary and Jesus away to somewhere safe, so the family moved to Egypt.

A secret message

Colour in the pictures.
Take the first letter of each word and fill in the boxes below!

1. mouse
2. elephant
3. ribbon
4. robin
5. yoyo
6. card
7. hat
8. robot
9. ice
10. sack
11. tree
12. man
13. apple
14. sleigh

m	1.	2.	3.	4.	5.

6.	7.	8.	9.	10.	11.	12.	a 13.	14.

Join the opposites

Draw a line with your pencil between the pictures that are the opposite of each other. The first is done for you.

Christmas character puppets

How to trace

1
Put the picture you want to trace on a flat surface.

2
Put a piece of tracing paper over the top. Keep it in place by using a paper clip or something to weigh it down. The tracing paper must stay in the same place while you work.

3
You should be able to see the lines of the picture through the tracing paper. Go over the lines with a soft pencil. Make your lines fairly thick and press fairly hard.

4
When you are sure you have gone over all the lines, and your picture looks complete, carefully remove the tracing paper.

5
Turn it over and with a very soft pencil, cover the back of the paper with lines.

6
Turn the paper back so the drawing is on the top.

7
Put it on a clean sheet of paper and hold it in place with a paper clip or weight, as before.

8
Now go over the lines once again with a pencil, pressing very hard. Do this slowly and carefully, making sure you do not miss out any lines.

9
Lift up the top piece of paper.

10
It is like magic! You should have a copy on the paper underneath. The copy is called a tracing.
It is a very clever way of making a copy of a picture you want to colour in, as you can make lots of tracings and still keep the picture in your book.

1

Now make a tracing of all the lines on the page.

2

Cut around the outer lines.

3

Cut out the finger holes.

4

Put two fingers through the holes and make the puppets come to life!

Choir boy

Santa Claus

Snowman

A Christmas carol

Ask your family to sing this carol with you on Christmas Day.

Away in a manger, no crib
  for a bed,
The little Lord Jesus
  laid down his sweet
  head.
The stars in the bright sky
  looked down where
  he lay,
The little Lord Jesus
  asleep on the hay.

The cattle are lowing,
  the baby awakes,
But little Lord Jesus no
  crying he makes.
I love you, Lord Jesus!
  Look down from the sky,
And stay by my bedside
  till morning is nigh.

Be near me, Lord Jesus: I
  ask you to stay
Close by me for ever and
  love me, I pray.
Bless all the dear children
  in your tender care.
And fit us for heaven to
  live with you there.

A very special baby

The story of the first Christmas is about the birth of a very special baby, and about the people who came to see him — the shepherds and the wise men. But it is only the beginning of a wonderful story.

Mary often thought about all the things that had happened when Jesus was born: the angel's message, the journey to Bethlehem, the shepherds and the wise men.

Mary and Joseph knew that the baby Jesus was special, that he was the son of God. But he looked like any other baby, and he needed his parents to care for him and love him.

Mary also knew that when Jesus grew up he would have special work to do — not just for her and for Joseph and for their small village; but for everyone.

What Mary did not yet know was that Jesus was not going to be a king on earth like any other king, but the king of a new kingdom of people who love him.

Today many, many people know about Jesus, and all over the world they celebrate at Christmas: it's like a very special birthday party.

Christmas is the time to be happy and to remember when one special baby was born: Jesus, the son of God.